GETTING INTO

Physiotherapy
Courses

FIRST EDITION

JAMES BURNETT and ANDREW LONG

KT-147-154

TROTMAN

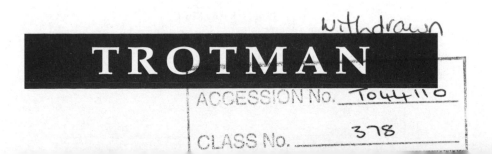

Getting into Physiotherapy Courses

This first edition published in 2002
by Trotman and Company Ltd
2 The Green, Richmond, Surrey TW9 1PL

© Trotman and Company Limited 2002

British Library Cataloguing in Publication Data
A catalogue record for this book is available from the
British Library.

ISBN 0 85660 818 1

Typeset by Mac Style Ltd, Scarborough, N. Yorkshire
Printed and bound in Great Britain
by Creative Print & Design (Wales) Ltd

CONTENTS

For the latest news on physiotherapy and physiotherapy courses go to www.mpw.co.uk/getintomed

ACKNOWLEDGEMENTS

We would like to thank Alice Holmes at the Chartered Society of Physiotherapy for her help in getting this project started, and Liz Boddy at Bryanston School who arranged for us to talk to physiotherapy students. We would also like to thank Katherine Cran, Tania Dawson and all of the other students who shared their experiences with us. Thank you also to Alex Babington for researching university courses and entrance requirements, to the university staff who provided us with information on their courses, and to everyone at Trotman and Company who allowed us to write this book.

The information in this book has come from a variety of sources and is, we believe, correct at the time of going to press. However, the views expressed are our own and any mistakes are down to us.

James Burnett and Andy Long

March 2002

The Student Book

2003

24th Edition
£14.99

0 85660 758 4

Student BOOK 2003

The Essential Guide for Applicants to UK Universities and Colleges

24th Edition

TROTMAN

www.careers-portal.co.uk

Klaus Boehm & Jenny Lees-Spalding

www.Careers-Portal.co.uk

Includes:

◆ **What it's like sections on all the UK's 280 institutions**

◆ **University/college department rankings**

◆ **Advice on all the major issues including drink, drugs and poverty**

The frankest and fullest guide to student life

The Sunday Telegraph

The straight-talking A-Z of Universities and Colleges

The Independent

INTRODUCTION

Most people associate physiotherapy with sport. Footballers are reported to be 'seeing the physio' after an injury, and the sight of a track-suited figure running on to the sports field carrying an aerosol spray and a sponge when a player is lying on the ground is a common one. For others, physiotherapy is something that takes place after an accident when the victim needs to learn to walk properly. However, whilst physiotherapy encompasses both of these, there are many other facets to the profession.

WHAT IS PHYSIOTHERAPY?

The human body is a complex machine that can go wrong for any number of reasons. Physiotherapy is a science-based medical subject that looks in detail at how the body moves, how muscles, bones, joints and ligaments work and how they react to pain and trauma. Physiotherapists diagnose numerous ailments that affect the muscles and nerves, and then proceed to treat the patient, ensuring independence, movement and a return to maximum performance. It is the physiotherapist's job not only to look at the problem and treat it but also to look for any predisposing factors that may have contributed to the patient's ailment and to advise on how to minimise the risk of the same thing happening again. Qualified physiotherapists work independently and as part of multidisciplinary teams ensuring that patients' health and mobility are improved.

WHAT DO PHYSIOTHERAPISTS DO?

Physiotherapists have numerous challenging roles within the health sector. They provide services such as rehabilitation and exercise before and after surgery. Within the wider community they provide services to adults with learning difficulties. They also have a role in the workplace

1

where they can help to reduce injuries such as Repetitive Strain Injury (RSI).

Chartered physiotherapists work with a wide range of people in many different environments both individually or as part of a large healthcare team. Physiotherapists deal with many different situations, which include:

- Teaching people the 'correct' ways to move and lift, in order to prevent or to slow the onset of problems such as back pain and RSI – see **Useful information**. This may also include helping athletes to avoid injury by discussing techniques and training programmes. Poor warm-up routines, too much training, poor equipment and incorrect technique are common causes of sporting injuries, all of which might be avoided. Using the idea that prevention is better than cure physiotherapists are able to show people that very small changes will be hugely beneficial, for example good footwear or the use of a wrist support when using a computer.
- Helping women before and after pregnancy by advising them about posture and exercise.
- Helping children to deal with mental and physical disabilities.
- Developing the potential of people with learning difficulties through exercise, sport and recreation; this could also include the use of specialist equipment.
- Helping people deal with stress and anxiety.
- Helping stroke victims recover movement in paralysed limbs.
- Helping orthopaedic patients after spinal operations or joint replacements and treating those debilitated following an accident. Using a variety of techniques to strengthen muscles and improve the mobility of individual joints, activities such as walking can be made much easier for people recovering from hip replacements or those with arthritis or osteoporosis. These methods can also reduce the pain and stiffness resulting from these conditions.
- Working with AIDS patients.
- Caring for the elderly who suffer from Parkinson's disease.
- Improving the confidence and self-esteem of those with mental illness through exercise and recreation, whilst also helping with relaxation and body awareness techniques.
- Working with the terminally ill or those in intensive care (inpatients and outpatients) to maintain movement and prevent respiratory problems.
- Helping sportsmen and sportswomen to recover from injury.

Physiotherapists use a range of techniques including:

- manipulation
- massage
- exercise
- hydrotherapy
- vibration
- ultrasound
- infrared and ultraviolet radiation.

Physiotherapy is not, however, a profession that only involves physical therapy. Physiotherapists work with people – in most cases people who are disabled, or who have been ill or injured. Physiotherapists need to be able to communicate on a personal level with people of all ages; to be reassuring and comforting; to explain the treatments they are using; and to help patients to overcome fear and pain. Physiotherapists need to be able to assess the needs of their patients and to be aware of the effects of external circumstances such as social or cultural factors.

WORKING AS A PHYSIOTHERAPIST

Physiotherapists work in a range of health and care environments that include hospitals, the local community, private practice, industry and sports settings. The majority are employed by the NHS. Physiotherapy comprises the largest group within the allied healthcare professions with over 30,000 state registered physiotherapists in the UK. To qualify as a registered physiotherapist you need to gain a degree from an approved degree course (see page 51) that has been validated by the Chartered Society of Physiotherapy (CSP) and the Council for Professions Supplementary to Medicine (CPSM). If you complete the degree you are then eligible for state registration (SRP) and Membership of the Chartered Society of Physiotherapy (MCSP). Career prospects for physiotherapists are excellent, with most graduates finding employment as soon as they complete their university courses.

HOW TO USE THIS BOOK

The competition for places on approved degree courses is intense – there are very few university courses that have more applicants per place than physiotherapy. There are more applicants per place for physiotherapy than for medicine, veterinary science or for courses at Oxford or Cambridge. Typically a university might receive over 1000 applications for 40 places. Even if each applicant makes six choices – and not all do – this still works out at more than four students chasing every place. As you will see on page 6, it is often far more than this. With such intense competition for places you need to think carefully about all stages of your application, from the preparation that you do before you apply through to the interview and the steps you take in order to maximise your chances of gaining a place should something go wrong at the examination stage.

This book is divided into four sections:

- Getting an interview
- Getting an offer
- Results day
- Useful information.

The first section deals with the preparation that you need to undertake in order to make your application as strong as possible. It includes advice on work experience, how to choose a university, and the UCAS form itself. The section on interviews provides tips on what to expect and on how to ensure that you come across as a potential physiotherapist. It also contains a checklist for you to tick off the important steps in making your application. The third section describes the steps that you need to take if you are holding an offer, or if you do not have an offer but want to gain a place through Clearing. The final section provides background information on physiotherapy and on physiotherapy issues.

Entry requirements are quoted in terms of A-level grades or UCAS points (the UCAS tariff) in this book. Information for students with Scottish Highers, IB, the BTEC National Diploma or the Irish Leaving Certificate is on page 45. The universities will be happy to provide you with further information on other qualifications.

On page 43 there is advice and information for 'non-standard' applicants – mature students, graduates and retake students.

As with other books in this series, including *Getting into Medical School* and *Getting into Dental School* this book is designed to be a route map for potential physiotherapists rather than a guide to physiotherapy as a profession. The Chartered Society of Physiotherapy, or physiotherapists whom you meet during work experience, should be the starting points for more detailed information on what being a physiotherapist entails. You should also consult Trotman's career guide *Getting into Physiotherapy*.

For the latest news on physiotherapy and physiotherapy courses go to www.mpw.co.uk/getintomed

GETTING AN INTERVIEW

In order to gain a place at university you have to submit a UCAS form. Before you do this, however, you need to be sure that you have investigated physiotherapy as thoroughly as you can. You need to do this for two reasons:

- you must be sure that physiotherapy is the right career for you; and
- you must demonstrate to the university admissions tutors that you are aware of the demands of the profession.

With so many applicants for every university place the selectors need to be sure that they do not 'waste' a place on someone who will then drop out of the course or the profession. For this reason the application has to be very convincing. Most people's exposure to physiotherapy is limited, and so you need to investigate the profession as thoroughly as you can.

When your UCAS form is received by the university it will not be on its own, but in a batch of, possibly, several hundred. It will have been reduced to about two-thirds of its original size, and the selectors will have to consider it, along with the others, in between the demands of their 'real' jobs. If your form is hard to read, uninteresting or lacking the things that the selector feels are important, it will be put on the 'reject without interview' pile. Nottingham University, for example, receives about 1600 applications, which have to be reduced to the 150 applicants to be called for interview. Of the 150 who might be interviewed about half of these might be made offers. A helpful step-by-step guide to the selection process used by Nottingham University can be found on www.nottingham.ac.uk/physiotherapy/undergraduate/selection.html.

You can only be called for interview on the basis of your UCAS form. The selectors will not know about the things that you have forgotten to say and they can only get an impression of you from what is on the form. We have come across too many good students who never got an interview simply because they did not think about the UCAS form: they relied on the fact that the selectors would somehow see through the words and get an instinctive feeling about them.

The following sections will tell you more about what the selectors are looking for, and how you can avoid common mistakes. Before looking at how the selectors go about deciding who to call to interview, however, there are a number of important things that you need to think about.

WORK EXPERIENCE

Without work experience your application will automatically be rejected. Nottingham University's physiotherapy website.

Work experience is vital if you are to be considered. Without evidence that you have worked with people in the community, preferably within the NHS, you will not be offered a place. Although not all universities are as explicit as Nottingham most will emphasise the need for work experience. For example, King's College London, in its website, states that applicants 'are advised to gain some work experience within a hospital prior to applying for a place', and Brunel University's website says that all applicants should undertake a period of physiotherapy clinical experience with a Chartered Physiotherapist.

Although work-shadowing physiotherapists in specialist areas such as sports clinics or private practices is useful experience it is generally not enough, and applicants without some contact with NHS hospitals are likely to find it hard to get an interview or an offer. If you are very lucky (and very determined) you may be able to get a paid job in an NHS hospital as a Physiotherapy Assistant. However, because of school or college commitments, this is usually only possible during a gap year. It is more likely that you will have to settle for an unpaid volunteer position either on a part-time basis (at weekends or in the evenings) or for a short period of time in the school holidays. If you are unable to arrange either of these you should try to shadow a physiotherapist for a day or two, and supplement this with a volunteer job in another caring environment such as an old people's home, a hospice, or in the children's ward of your local hospital.

Whilst there are no rules about the minimum length of time that you should spend doing work experience, volunteer work or work-shadowing, as a general rule the candidates who can demonstrate commitment by doing something on a regular basis throughout the year or who have spent at least two weeks in a hospital environment are likely to be in the strongest position. Some schools operate schemes where they arrange this for you. This saves you the hard work of contacting hospitals or clinics, but the disadvantage is that you will be unable to impress the selectors with your dynamism and determination because you will not be able to say '*I arranged my work experience myself*'.

If your school does not operate such a scheme you have two options: to use any contacts that your family or friends have; or to approach local hospitals. To do this you need to get the names and addresses of local hospitals with physiotherapy departments and physiotherapy clinics from the telephone directory. You can also find lists of physiotherapists on the Internet. One such site is www.therapy-world.co.uk/physio.htm. You should write a formal letter, and include the name of a referee, someone who can vouch for your interest in physiotherapy as well as to your reliability. Your careers teacher, housemaster/mistress or form teacher would be ideal. An example of a suitable letter is given opposite.

As well as helping you to decide whether you are serious about physiotherapy and adding weight to your application, you may be able to get one of the people you work with to give you a reference in order to help your application.

CASE STUDY

Katherine

Katherine is in her first year at the University of Hertfordshire. She was unsuccessful in her first application for physiotherapy and decided to take a gap year, and to use it to gain more work experience in order to strengthen her application. 'Physiotherapy appealed to me because it was a practical job, rather than being academically based. I had always been interested in science and biology in particular, and come from a medical background. I had seen both my parents treat patients in different ways and get great satisfaction from it, and I felt that it was something I wanted to do.'

Katherine's work experience included three weeks as a physiotherapy assistant, and another three days shadowing physiotherapists at her local hospital. During her gap year she worked as a physiotherapy assistant in a school for children with severe physical disabilities. This was a challenging position but it convinced her that she was right in applying for physiotherapy. After graduating Katherine is aiming to specialise in either outpatients, orthopaedics or respiratory physiotherapy.

'Get as much experience as you can – it doesn't just have to be as a physio assistant. Be determined: there is always a way to get in if you really want to' is Katherine's advice for prospective physiotherapists.

Mr P Mackie [Telephone the hospital to find the name of the person who organises volunteers.]
Volunteer Coordinator
Physiotherapy Department
Melchester General Hospital
123 High Street
Melchester
Postcode
Date

Dear Mr Mackie
I am in the first year of my A-level studies, and I am interested in a career in physiotherapy. In order to find out more about physiotherapy I would like to work as a volunteer in the physiotherapy department. I would be able to work on Wednesday afternoons, Saturday afternoons and all day Sunday for the rest of this year. I would be extremely grateful if you would be prepared to meet me, in order to discuss whether it would be possible for me to spend some time at Melchester General Hospital.

If you require a reference, please contact my careers teacher. His address is:

Mr N Townson
Head of Careers
Melchester High School
Melchester
Postcode

I look forward to hearing from you.

Yours sincerely
[Your signature]
[Your name]

Things to look out for during work experience

The variety of treatments available to patients

Make sure that you know what you are observing. Ask the physiotherapist or nurse for the technical names of the procedures that you see, and for information on the techniques and equipment used. Ask about the advantages and disadvantages of different types of treatments, and in what situations they are used. Keep a diary of what you saw on a day-to-day basis so that you can use it to revise from before an interview. There are a number of websites that provide detailed information on medical conditions and treatments, and you could add further detail to your diary using one of these. You will find the addresses at the end of this book.

Working as a physiotherapist

Ask the physiotherapist about his/her life. Find out about the hours, how much physiotherapists are paid, the demands of the job, and the career options open to physiotherapists. Find out what the physiotherapists like about the job, and what they dislike.

CASE STUDY

Adam

Adam first thought of physiotherapy as a possible career when he realised that he was never going to play cricket for England. 'It was never a realistic option because I was never very good at cricket, but I loved sport and I wanted to be involved in it. By the time I was 13 I realised that, if I couldn't make the school team, I certainly wouldn't get a call from England!'

'I got two A grades at GCSE, and the rest were Bs and Cs. I decided to take biology, economics and sports science for A-level, and physics as an AS-level. I found them hard but I knew that I needed BBB to get into Nottingham, my first choice. Someone at school told me that I had to get work experience so I arranged to shadow the physiotherapist at my local football team for three days. Just before I applied I went to an open day and was told that I would probably be rejected because my work experience was insufficient. My form teacher's wife worked at a hospital nearby so she was able to get me into the physiotherapy department there as an assistant very quickly. If I hadn't been to the open day, and been lucky that I had a contact in an NHS physiotherapy department, I wouldn't even have been interviewed.'

Adam's interviews concentrated on his work experience: 'they really probed me about what being a physiotherapist is really like – not just what I did, but what it is like working as a physiotherapist day in and day out, so I'm glad I did it'. Adam received two offers from his four physiotherapy choices. He was not confident about the grades he was going to get, so he put down two other choices – sports science and sports management – where the grade requirements were lower. The work experience convinced him that he desperately wanted to become a physiotherapist. 'I didn't really know what physiotherapy was about, even though I had applied to study it, before I did my work experience. I thought that it was a glamorous job where you worked with sportsmen, got to see sport for free, and spent most of the day chatting about sport. The spell in the hospital showed me what it really entails. Dealing with stroke victims, or old people who don't know what is happening to them, is not easy. You need lots of patience and to really want to make a difference to them. I will probably end up working in a sport-related environment, but I am more open-minded now than I was before.' Adam achieved the ABB that he needed, and is now in his first year at Nottingham.

Tips for work experience

- Dress as the physiotherapists dress: be clean, tidy and reasonably formal.
- Offer to help the physiotherapist or the nurses with routine tasks.
- Show an interest in all that is going on around you.

CHOICE OF UNIVERSITIES

Once you have completed your work experience, and are sure that you want to be a physiotherapist, you need to research your choice of university. There are various factors that you should take into account:

- the type of course
- the entrance requirements (see page 54)
- location
- whether you would be taught alongside students on other healthcare courses such as radiology, nursing, occupational therapy or podiatry.

The next step is to get hold of the prospectuses. If your school does not have spare copies telephone the universities, which will send you copies free of charge. Most universities have very informative websites that carry extra information on admissions policies. Once you have narrowed down the number of universities to, say, six or seven, you should try to visit them in order to get a better idea of what studying there will be like.

Your school careers department will have details of open days (or you could telephone the universities directly), and some universities will arrange for you to be shown around at other times of the year as well. Don't simply select your universities because someone tells you that they have good reputations or that they are easier to get into, because you will be spending the next three or four years of your life at one of them, and if you do not like the place you are unlikely to last the course.

Apart from talking to current or ex-physiotherapy students or careers advisers, there are a number of other sources of information to help you to choose. The *Guardian* newspaper publishes its own league table of universities, ranked by a total score that combines the university's teaching assessment, a 'value-added' score based on the class of degree obtained compared to A-level (or equivalent) grades, spending on facilities and materials, student/staff ratio, job prospects and entrance requirements. The *Financial Times* also compiles its own table. The tables can be found at http://education-guardian.co.uk/university guide/ and http://specials-ft.com/universities2001/. Of course league tables only tell you a small part of the whole story, and anyone who makes their choices solely on this basis without visiting the universities or reading the prospectuses is taking a serious risk.

ACADEMIC REQUIREMENTS

In addition to the grades required at A-level and AS-level, all of the universities specify the minimum grades that they require at GCSE. This varies from university to university, but it is unlikely that you will be considered unless you have at least five or six GCSE grades, including science, English and mathematics, taken at one sitting and at B grade or above. If your grades fall below these requirements you need to get your referee to comment on them, either to explain why you underperformed (illness, family disruption etc) or why they expect your A-level performance to be better than your GCSE grades indicate.

Students following the A-level system should also work hard to ensure that they gain good grades at AS-level. Under the old A-level system the first year of the sixth form (year 12) could be a time for adjustment, contemplation and relaxation. Even if you studied modular A-levels the marks did not feature on your UCAS form, and modules could be retaken again and again. The new system puts pressure on you from the start, since not only do the grades appear on the form but also many of the medical schools will specify minimum grade requirements. Even those that don't will consciously or subconsciously use them as an indicator of your likely A-level grades.

Imagine the situation: the selector has one more interview slot to fill, and has the choice between two students with identical work experience, GCSE results and A-level predictions; but one has scored DDDD at AS-level, the other achieved AAAA. Who do you think will get the place?

The other thing to bear in mind is that a score of DDDD is unlikely to lead to BBB at A-level since an AS contributes 50 per cent of the total A-level marks, and so the selectors may doubt that the predicted grades are achievable. What this will do is give admissions tutors more to go on than GCSE grades and A-level predictions alone, since the AS grades will be published in the August preceding your application and can feature on your UCAS form. It is possible that most universities will specify a minimum AS-level requirement for applicants. For the student, this means that the first year of A-levels is as important as the second, and the days of the lower sixth being seen as a relaxed year are over.

Entrance requirements vary from university to university, but a 'standard' offer might ask for a minimum of 300 points from 21 units to include three 6-unit awards or equivalent. The offer would probably specify that biology must be studied to A2 level, along with one other science. This would be satisfied by a student who gained BBC at A-level (6-unit awards) and E at AS-level (3-unit award). You should also check the university prospectuses for details of A-level and AS-level requirements. Some universities, for example, specify that they require one of the AS subjects to be an art or humanity, rather than all science/mathematics.

YOUR CHOICES

There are six spaces on the UCAS form, and unlike applications for medicine, dentistry or veterinary science, where only four of these can be used to select universities, all six can be used for physiotherapy courses. You do not have to fill all six spaces with physiotherapy courses. You are allowed to apply for a mixture of physiotherapy courses and non-physiotherapy courses, or to leave spaces blank. If you are worried that you might not be offered a place to study physiotherapy and you would consider other courses you might want to put down four physiotherapy courses and two other courses. The two non-physiotherapy courses should be related to physiotherapy, either directly (occupational therapy, podiatry) or in a related discipline such as human biology, physiology, radiology or nursing. You should not enter fewer than four physiotherapy courses on the form because if you do you are unlikely to convince the selectors that you are genuinely committed. Whatever you do, do not put down medicine or veterinary science as your other choices, because not only will the university or veterinary school reject you, but it will be obvious to the selectors that you are not committed to physiotherapy. If you decide that you would be happy to accept an alternative to physiotherapy if you are unsuccessful, by all means choose another course as long as you feel able to justify the choice at interview. However, our advice is to apply only to physiotherapy courses because:

- It demonstrates to the selectors that you are committed to becoming a physiotherapist.
- You do not run the risk of having to accept a place on a course that you do not wish to take. If you are unsuccessful in your initial application for physiotherapy you might be able to gain a place through Clearing, as long as you have not accepted something else.

Once you have made your final choices make sure that you have entered the details on to the form correctly. More advice on this can be found in the MPW guide *How to Complete Your UCAS Form*.

PERSONAL STATEMENT

The personal statement is your chance to show the selectors that:

- You have thought about why you want to be a physiotherapist.
- You have investigated the profession.
- You are the right sort of person for their university.

14

Before we look at how you go about doing this, a word of warning. If the selectors cannot read your personal statement all of your hard work and preparation will have been wasted. Unless your handwriting is very neat, and is clear and legible when reduced to two-thirds of its original size, word-process your personal statement, and print or photocopy it on to the form. About 30 per cent of UCAS forms are now submitted electronically using the Electronic Application System (EAS). If your school offers this you should use it since it not only speeds up the whole process but also has a number of checks incorporated into it to stop you making silly mistakes with examination boards and dates.

The personal statement is your opportunity to demonstrate to the selectors that you have not only researched physiotherapy thoroughly, but also that you have the right personal qualities to succeed as a physiotherapist. Do not be tempted to write the statement in the sort of formal English that you find in, for example, job applications. Read through a draft of your statement, and ask yourself the question *'Does it sound like me?'* If not, rewrite it. Avoid phrases such as *'I was fortunate enough to be able to shadow a physiotherapist...'* when you really mean *'I shadowed a physiotherapist...'* or *'I arranged to shadow a physiotherapist...'*

Why physiotherapy?

A high proportion of UCAS forms contain the phrase *'From an early age I have wanted to be a physiotherapist because it is the only career that combines my love of science with the chance to work with people'.* Admissions tutors not only get bored with reading this, but it is also clearly untrue: if you think about it, there are many careers that combine science and people, including teaching, pharmacy, dentistry and nursing. However, the basic ideas behind this sentence may well apply to you. If so, you need to personalise it. You could mention an incident that first got you interested in physiotherapy – a visit to a physiotherapist, a conversation with a family friend or a lecture at school, for instance. You could write about your interest in human biology, or a biology project that you undertook when you were younger to illustrate your interest in science, and you could give examples of how you like to work with others. The important thing is to back up your initial interest in physiotherapy with your efforts to investigate the career.

What have you done to investigate physiotherapy?

This is where you describe your work experience. It is important to demonstrate that you gained something from the work experience, and that it has given you an insight into the profession. You should give an indication of the length of time that you spent at each work placement, what treatments you observed, and your impressions of physiotherapy. You could comment on what aspects of physiotherapy attract you, what you found interesting, or on something that surprised you.

Here is an example of a description of a student's work experience that would not have impressed the selectors:

I spent three days at my local hospital's physiotherapy ward. I saw some patients having ultrasounds, and a man who went in the hydrotherapy pool. It was very interesting.

The example below would have been much more convincing because it is clear that the student was interested in what was happening.

During my three weeks at Melchester General Hospital I was able to shadow two physiotherapists. I watched a range of treatments including ultrasound and exercise in the hydrotherapy pool. I was particularly interested in the ultrasound treatment because I had only ever seen it used for diagnosis. In the cases that I saw during my work experience it was used to stimulate healing in muscle tissue that had been damaged in an accident. Most of the patients that I saw receiving treatment were elderly. I was able to spend some time with a man who had suffered a stroke and had limited use of his hands. The physiotherapist worked with him on a series of repetitive exercises to try to get him to be able to perform simple tasks. I was also able to see the importance of teamwork because the physiotherapist worked alongside a speech therapist as the man had also lost the ability to communicate effectively.

With luck, the selectors may pick on this at interview, and ask questions about the methods that the physiotherapists used, and you could then bring in your knowledge of ultrasound (which you had investigated following your work experience).

Personal qualities

As a physiotherapist you will be working with others throughout your career. To qualify as a physiotherapist you will study alongside maybe 30 others in your year, for three years. The person reading your UCAS form has to decide two things: whether you have the right personal qualities to become a successful physiotherapist, and whether you will cope with and contribute to university life. To be a successful physiotherapist you need to be able to relate to other people; to survive and enjoy university you need to be able to get on with a wide range of people too. Unlike school life, where many of the activities are organised and arranged by the teachers, all of the social activities at university are instigated and organised by the students. For this reason the selectors are looking for people who have the enthusiasm and ability to motivate others, and are prepared to give up their own time to arrange sporting, dramatic, musical or social activities.

How, then, does the person reading your personal statement know whether you have the qualities that they are looking for? They will expect to read about some of the following:

- participation in team events
- involvement in school plays or concerts
- positions of responsibility
- work in the local community
- part-time or holiday jobs
- charity work.

The selectors will be aware that some schools offer more in the way of activities and responsibilities than others, and they will make allowances for this. You don't have to have been on a school expedition to India or to be Head Girl to be considered, but you need to be able to demonstrate that you have taken the best possible advantage of what is on offer. The selectors will be aware of the type of school or college that you have come from (there is a box on the back of the UCAS form that your referee fills in) and, consequently, the opportunities that are open to you. What they are looking for is that you have grasped these opportunities.

A sample personal statement

Why physiotherapy?

I first became interested in becoming a physiotherapist following treatment for a knee injury. This interest was confirmed after attending a seminar given to our school Science Society on biomechanics, and by undertaking several work experience placements. In my local hospital I worked alongside physiotherapists on a neurological rehabilitation ward and was able to observe hydrotherapy treatment and also the treatment of children with cystic fibrosis. I have been helping with a wide range of exercise programmes both in and out of the hydrotherapy pool, and have benefited from the training on subjects that are relevant to children. I have also been involved in teaching swimming to children with learning disabilities and visiting elderly people. This range of experience has helped me to understand the differing demands placed on therapists; the importance of mutual trust, teamwork and the place of physiotherapy within healthcare.

Activities and responsibilities

I participate in many sports, am captain of the school 1st VII netball team and have also played for the 1st XI hockey team. I enjoy textiles and have made several rugs and items of clothing. I like photography, particularly the work of Ansell Adams who photographed landscapes, and his work has inspired me to go to a number of national parks to take pictures. I go to the cinema and theatre as often as I can and I like music. I have taken grade 7 on the clarinet and am learning the guitar, which I play badly in a band that I formed with some friends. We have yet to play in public! For my gap year I have arranged to spend six months working in a school for children with serious physical disabilities, and I will then travel with friends to India, Thailand and Vietnam.

THE REFERENCE

As well as your GCSE results and your personal statement, the selectors will take your reference into account. This is where your head, housemaster or head of sixth form writes about what an outstanding person you are, the life and soul of the school; how you are on target for three A grades at A-level; and why you will become an outstanding physiotherapist. For him or her to say this, of course, it has to be true. The referee is expected to be as honest as possible, and to try to accurately assess your character and potential. You may believe that you have all of the qualities, academic and personal, necessary in a physiotherapist, but unless you have demonstrated these to your teachers they will be unable to support your application. Ideally your efforts to impress them will have begun at the start of the sixth form (or before): you will have become involved in school activities, you will have been working hard at your studies and you will be popular with students and teachers alike. However, it is never too late, and some people mature later than others, so if this does not sound like you start to make efforts to impress the people who will contribute to your reference.

As part of the reference your referee will need to predict the grades that you are likely to achieve. As you will see from the table on page 54 most universities ask for at least BBB. If you are predicted lower than this it is unlikely that you will be considered. Talk to your teachers and find out whether you are on target for these grades. If not, you need to either a) work harder or more effectively – and make sure that your teachers notice that you are doing so, b) get some extra help either at school or outside, for instance by taking an Easter revision course or c) delay submitting your UCAS form until you have your A-level results. If you decide on this option make sure that you use your gap year wisely (see below).

WHEN TO SUBMIT THE UCAS FORM

The closing date for receipt of the form by UCAS is 15 January. Late applications are accepted by UCAS, but the universities are not obliged to consider them, and because of the pressure on places it is unlikely that late applications will be considered. Although you can submit your form any time between the beginning of September and the December deadline (remembering to get it to your referee at least two weeks before the deadline so that he/she has time to prepare the reference), most admissions tutors admit that the earlier the form is submitted the better your chance of being called for interview. Your best bet is to talk to the person who will deal with the form in the summer term of your first year of A-levels, and work on your personal statement and choice of universities over the summer holidays so that it is ready to hand in at the start of the September term.

DEFERRED ENTRY

Most admissions tutors are happy to consider students who take a gap year, and many encourage it. However, if you are considering this, you need to make sure that you are going to use the time constructively. A year spent watching daytime TV is not going to impress anybody, whereas independent travelling, charity or voluntary work either at home or abroad, work experience or a responsible job will all indicate that you have used the time to develop independence and maturity. Above all, make sure that whatever you do with the year involves regular contact with other people.

You can either apply for deferred entry when you submit your UCAS form, in which case you need to outline your plans in your personal statement, or apply in September following the publication of your A-level results. If you expect to be predicted the right grades, and the feedback from your school or college is that you will be given a good reference, you should apply for deferred entry; but if you are advised by your referee that you are unlikely to be considered you should give yourself more time to work on your referees by waiting until you have your A-level results.

WHAT HAPPENS NEXT?

When the staff at UCAS receive your form they will send you an acknowledgement, either the self-addressed postcard that you sent with the form, or confirmation if you submitted the form by e-mail. About two weeks later you will receive a statement of entry, which lists all of your choices. Check this carefully – make sure that the universities and course codes are correct, and that your name and address are also correct. Remember also to inform UCAS if you change address.

The next correspondence you will receive, if you are lucky, is likely to be from the universities, asking you to attend an interview. Don't be alarmed if you do not hear anything soon after UCAS has sent you your statement of entry. Some universities interview on a first come, first served basis whilst others wait until all applications are in before deciding who to interview. It is not uncommon for students to hear nothing until after Christmas.

If you are unlucky you will receive a slip from UCAS telling you that you have been rejected by one or more of the universities. Don't despair: you may hear better news from another of the places that you applied to. Even if you get six rejections the worst thing that you can do is give up and decide that it is no longer worth working hard. On the contrary, if this does happen, you should become even more determined to gain high grades so that you can apply either through Clearing, or the following year. The process of making Clearing applications is discussed on page 36.

CHECKLIST

- ☐ At least two weeks' NHS work-shadowing?
- ☐ Voluntary work?
- ☐ Right GCSEs?
- ☐ On target for required grades?
- ☐ Looked at all universities' prospectuses?
- ☐ Open days?
- ☐ Minimum four physiotherapy choices on UCAS form?
- ☐ Does your personal statement demonstrate commitment, research, personal qualities, communication skills and manual dexterity?

GETTING AN OFFER

If the selectors like the picture that the UCAS form has painted of you they will call you for interview. The purpose of the interview is to allow them to see whether this picture is an accurate one, and to investigate whether you have a genuine interest in physiotherapy. The interviewers will generally ask you three types of question:

1. those designed to relax you so that they can assess your communication skills;
2. those designed to investigate your interest and suitability for physiotherapy;
3. those designed to get a clearer picture of your personal qualities.

INTERVIEW QUESTIONS

Questions to get you relaxed

How was your journey here today?

The interviewers are not really interested in the details of your journey. Do not be tempted to give them a minute-by-minute account of your bus journey ('*...and then we waited for six minutes at the road works on Corporation Street...*'), or to simply say '*OK*'. Say something like '*It was fine, thank you. The train journey took about two hours, which gave me the chance to catch up on some reading*'. With a bit of luck they will ask you what you read, which gives you the chance to talk about a book, newspaper article or an item in *New Scientist*.

I am interested to know why you decided to apply to Melchester?

Another variation on this might be '*How did you narrow your choice down to six universities?*' The panel will be looking for evidence of research, and that your reasons are based on informed judgement.

Probably the best possible answer would start with '*I came to your open day ...*' because you can then proceed to tell them why you like their university so much, what impressed you about the course and facilities and how the atmosphere of the place would particularly suit you. Even if you are unable to attend open days try to arrange a formal or informal visit before you are interviewed so that you can show that you are aware of the environment, both academic and physical, and that you like the place. If you know people who are at the university or on the course so much the better. You should also know about the course structure. On page 46 there is an overview of the differences and similarities between courses, and the prospectus will give detailed information. Given the choice between a candidate who is not only going to make a good physiotherapist, but clearly wants to come to their institution, and another who may have the right qualities but does not seem to care whether it is there or somewhere else that he/she studies, who do you think the selectors will choose?

Answers to avoid are '*Reputation*' unless you know in detail the areas for which the university is highly regarded; '*It's in London, and I don't want to move away from my friends*'; '*You take a lot of retake students*'; or '*My dad says it is easy to get a place here*'.

A good answer could be '*I came to an open day last summer, which is why I have applied here. I enjoyed the day, and was impressed by the facilities, and by the comments of the students who showed us around because they seemed so enthusiastic about the course. Also, my cousin studied English at the university and I visited her, and got to sample the atmosphere of the town.*'

There are variations on this question. The interviewers may ask you what you know about the course, or about the university. In all cases this is your chance to show the interviewers that you are desperate to come to their university.

A word of warning: do your homework by reading the prospectus and looking at the website. Although on the surface all physiotherapy courses appear to cover broadly the same subjects, there are big differences between the way the courses are delivered, and in the opportunities for patient contact, and your interviewers will expect you to know about their course.

Questions about physiotherapy

Why do you want to be a physiotherapist?

The question that all interviewees expect. Given that the interviewers will be aware that you are expecting the question, they will also expect your answer to be carefully planned. If you look surprised, and say something like *'Um...well...I haven't really thought about why...'* you can expect to be rejected. Other answers to avoid are: *'The money'*; *'I couldn't get into medicine'*; *'I want to help people'*; *'I want to work for Arsenal'*.

Many students are worried that they will sound insincere when they answer this question. The way to avoid this is to try to bring in reasons that are personal to you, for instance an incident that started your interest (perhaps a visit to a physiotherapist), or an aspect of your work experience that particularly fascinated you. The important thing is to try to express clearly what interested you rather than try to generalise your answers. Rather than say *'Physiotherapy combines science, working with people and the chance to have control over your career'* – which says little about you, tell the interviewers about the way that your interest progressed. An example of a good answer:

> *'Although it seemed strange to my friends, I used to enjoy going with my grandfather to a physiotherapist when he had difficulty in walking due to arthritis. This was because the physiotherapist explained things very clearly and patiently, and I was interested in what was happening around me. My favourite subject is biology, particularly the anatomy side of it, and I always wanted to do something that involved this. When I was thinking about my career I arranged to shadow another physiotherapist, and the more time I spent at the hospital the more I realised that this would really suit me. This also gave me the chance to find out about what being a physiotherapist is really like. The things about physiotherapy that I particularly enjoy are...'*

Warning: do not learn this passage and repeat it at your interview. Ensure that your answer is not only personal to you, but also honest.

24

With luck, the interviewers will pick up on something that you said about work experience, and ask you more questions about this.

Since *'Why do you want to be a physiotherapist?'* is such an obvious question, interviewers often try to find out the information in different ways. Expect questions such as *'When did your interest in physiotherapy start?'*, or *'What was it about your work experience that finally convinced you that physiotherapy was for you?'*

I see that you spent two weeks with your physiotherapist. Was there anything that surprised you?

Variations on this question could include *'Was there anything that particularly interested you?'*, *'Was there anything you found off-putting?'* or simply *'Tell me about your work experience'*. What these questions really mean is *'Are you able to show us that you were interested in what was happening during your work experience?'* Returning to the original question, answering either *'Yes'* or *'No'* without explanation will not gain you many marks. Similarly, saying *'Yes, I was surprised by the number of patients who seemed very scared'* says nothing about your awareness of the physiotherapist's approach to his/her patients. However, answering *'Yes, I was surprised by the number of patients who seemed very scared. What struck me, however, was the way in which the physiotherapist dealt with each patient as an individual, sometimes being sympathetic, sometimes explaining things in great detail and sometimes using humour to relax them. For instance...'* shows that you were interested enough to be aware of more than the most obvious things. Sentences that start with *'For example...'* and *'For instance...'* are particularly important as they allow you to demonstrate your interest. In order to be able to give examples you should keep a diary of things that you saw during your work experience so that you do not forget. You should revise from this before your interview, as if you were revising for an examination.

I see that you try to keep up to date with developments in physiotherapy. Can you tell me about something that you have read about recently?

If you are interested in making physiotherapy your career the selectors will expect you to be interested enough in the subject to want to read about it. Good sources of information are the many websites for medical and physiotherapy professionals (addresses are given at the end of the book), *New Scientist*, the Chartered Society of Physiotherapy's website and the national newspapers. You should get into the habit of looking at a broadsheet newspaper every day to see if there are any medically or physiotherapy-related stories. Note that the question uses the word recently: recent does not mean an article you read two years ago – keep up to date. You could, for instance, say *'There was a recent report that sportsmen and women risk injury from air-filled training shoes. There was a survey of basketball players which showed that they were four times more likely to suffer ankle injuries if they were wearing trainers with soles that contained air pockets.'*

During your work experience, you had the chance to discuss physiotherapy with physiotherapists. What do you know about the career opportunities and pay for physiotherapists?

You must make sure that you do some research on career paths by asking questions about this when you meet physiotherapists. Most physiotherapists work in the NHS, but there are many other options. On page 1 we described many of the types of work undertaken by physiotherapists. Most physiotherapists end up specialising in one or more particular areas – in most cases as a result of an interest that grew during their training. The best answer to a question like this is to describe the career paths of physiotherapists you have met and worked with, as this will allow you to highlight your own work experience.

What qualities should a physiotherapist possess?

These have been discussed on page 17. However, don't simply list them. The question has not been asked because the interviewer is puzzled about what these qualities are; it has been asked to give you a chance to show a) that you are aware of them, and b) that you possess them. The best way to answer this is to use phrases such as *'During my work experience at the Melchester Physiotherapy Clinic I was able to observe/talk to the physiotherapist, and I became aware that…'*, or *'Communication is very important. For instance, when I was shadowing my physiotherapist, there was a patient who…'* Try always to relate these general questions to your own experiences.

Physiotherapy requires high levels of physical fitness and manual dexterity. Do you possess these?

Manual manipulation of a patient's limbs requires a fair degree of fitness and strength, and as a physiotherapist you will need to be able to help to lift and lower patients. If you have trouble picking up a coffee cup without breathing heavily for the next ten minutes physiotherapy may not be the best career for you. The interviewers will need to be reassured that you are able to work in a physically demanding environment, and also that you have the manual dexterity necessary to perform sometimes intricate tasks. Try to anticipate this question by preparing an answer which demonstrates that you have these qualities. Sport is always a good indicator of fitness and coordination, but you could also mention situations that you encountered during your work experience, demanding tasks that you perform as part of a weekend job, expeditions that you have been on at school as part of the Duke of Edinburgh Award, or a hobby such as DIY.

> **Warning: Do not lie about the example you describe. An admissions tutor I talked to recounted the story of an applicant who wrote on the UCAS form that he worked for a local Riding for the Disabled scheme. However, the previous interview had been with someone from the same town who had explained that there was no such scheme in the area, which is why she could not carry on doing this when she moved into the area. He was found out, and rejected.**

Questions to find out about what sort of person you are

What do you do to relax?

Don't say 'Watch TV' or 'Go to the pub'. Mention something that involves working or communicating with others, for instance sport or music. Use the question to demonstrate that you possess the qualities required in a physiotherapist. However, don't make your answer so insincere that the interviewers realise that you are trying to impress them. Saying 'I relax most effectively when I go to the local physiotherapy clinic to shadow the physiotherapist' will not convince them.

How do you cope with stress?

Physiotherapy can be a stressful occupation. Physiotherapists have to deal with difficult people, those who are scared and those who react badly when in a physiotherapy ward. For many people physiotherapy can be painful and distressing and patients are not always cooperative, or even aware of why they are receiving treatment. In these circumstances the physiotherapist cannot panic, but must remain calm and rational. The interviewers will want to make a judgement as to whether you will be able to cope with the demands of the job.

Having been through it themselves, it is unlikely that they will regard school examinations as being particularly stressful. Hard work, yes, but not as stressful as training to be a physiotherapist or practising as a physiotherapist. What they are looking for are answers that demonstrate your calmness and composure when dealing with others. You could relate it to your work experience, or your Saturday job. Dealing with a queue of angry and impatient customers demanding to know why their cheeseburgers are not ready can be difficult. Other areas that can provide evidence of stress management are school expeditions, public speaking, or positions of responsibility at school or outside.

I see that you enjoy reading. What is the most recent book that you have read?

The question might be about the cinema or theatre, but the point of it is the same: to get you talking about something that interests you. Although it may sound obvious, if you have written that you enjoy reading on your UCAS form make sure that you have actually read something recently. Admissions tutors will be able to tell you stories about interviewees who look at them with absolute amazement when they are asked about books, despite it featuring in the personal statement. Answers such as '*Well...I haven't had much time recently, but...let me see...I read* Elle *last month, and...oh yes...I had to read* Jane Eyre *for my English GCSE*' will do your chances no good at all. By all means put down that you like reading, but make sure that you have read an interesting novel in the period leading up to the interview, and be prepared to discuss it.

HOW TO SUCCEED IN YOUR INTERVIEW

You should prepare for an interview as if you are preparing for an examination. This involves revision of your work experience diary so that you can recount details of your time with physiotherapists, revision of the newspaper, website and *New Scientist* articles that you have saved and revision of all of the things that you have mentioned on your personal statement. When you are preparing for your A-levels you sit a mock examination so that the real thing does not come as a total surprise; when you are preparing for an interview have a mock interview so that you can get some feedback on your answers. Your school may be able to help you. If not, independent sixth-form colleges usually provide a mock interview service. Friends of your parents may also be able to help. If possible, video your mock interview so that you are aware of the way you come across in an interview situation. There is a list of practice interview questions below.

MOCK INTERVIEW QUESTIONS

1. Why do you want to be a physiotherapist?
2. What have you done to investigate physiotherapy?
3. Why does physiotherapy interest you more than medicine/nursing/radiography?
4. What are the ideal qualities that a physiotherapist should possess?
5. Do you possess these qualities?
6. Give me an example of how you cope with stress.
7. Why did you apply to this university?
8. Did you come to our open day?
9. During your work experience, did anything surprise you?
10. During your work experience, did anything shock you?
11. Was the physiotherapist you shadowed good at communicating with his/her patients?
12. Tell me about preventive physiotherapy.
13. What is occupational therapy?
14. What is repetitive strain injury?
15. What is cystic fibrosis/a stroke/arthritis?
16. What is hydrotherapy?
17. What is ultrasound and how is it used?

18. Is exercise always good for you?
19. How much do NHS physiotherapists earn?
20. Have you read any articles about physiotherapy recently?
21. What advances can we expect in physiotherapy technology/treatment in the future?
22. What have you done to demonstrate your commitment to the community?
23. What would you contribute to this university?
24. What are your best/worst qualities?
25. What was the last novel you read? Did you like it?
26. What was the last play/film you saw? Did you like it?
27. What do you do to relax?
28. What is your favourite A-level subject?
29. What grades do you expect to gain in your A-levels?
30. What precautions need to be taken with patients who are HIV positive?
31. How does teamwork apply to the role of a physiotherapist?

Appearance and body language are important. The impression you create can be very influential. Remember that if the interviewers cannot picture you as a physiotherapist in future years they are unlikely to offer you a place.

Body Language

- Maintain eye contact with the interviewers.
- Direct most of what you are saying to the person who asked you the question, but occasionally look around at the others on the panel.
- Sit up straight, but adopt a position that you feel comfortable in.
- Don't wave your hands around too much, but don't keep them gripped together to stop them moving. Fold them across your lap, or rest them on the arms of the chair.

Speech

- Talk slowly and clearly.
- Don't use slang.
- Avoid saying *'Erm...'*, *'You know'*, *'Sort of'*.
- Say hello at the start of the interview, and thank you and goodbye at the end.

Dress and appearance

- Wear clothes that show you have made an effort for the interview. You do not have to wear a business suit, but a jacket and tie (men), or a skirt and blouse (women) are appropriate.
- Make sure that you are clean and tidy.
- If appropriate, shave before the interview (but avoid overpowering aftershave).
- Clean your nails and shoes.
- Wash your hair.
- Avoid (visible) piercings, earrings (men), jeans and trainers.

At the end of the interview

You may be given the opportunity to ask a question at the end of the interview. Bear in mind that the interviews are carefully timed, and that your attempts to impress the panel with 'clever' questions may do quite the opposite. The golden rule is: only ask a question if you are genuinely interested in the answer (and which, of course, you were unable to find during your careful reading of the prospectus).

Questions to avoid

- *'What is the structure of the first year of the course?'*
- *'Will I be able to live in a hall of residence?'*
- *'When will I first have contact with patients?'*

As well as being boring questions, the answers to these will be available in the prospectus. You have obviously not done any serious research.

Questions you could ask

- *'I haven't studied physics AS-level. Do you think I should go through some physics textbooks before the start of the course?'*
  This shows that you are keen, and that you want to make sure that you can cope with the course. It will give the selectors a chance to talk about the extra course they offer for non-physicists.
- *'Do you think I should try to get more work experience before the start of the course?'*
  Again, an indication of your keenness.

- *'Earlier, I couldn't answer the question you asked me on ultrasound. What is the answer?'*
  Something that you genuinely might want to know.
- *'How soon will you let me know if I have been successful or not?'*
  Something you really want to know.

STRUCTURING THE INTERVIEW

> **Remember: if in doubt, don't ask a question. End by saying 'All of my questions have been answered by the prospectus and the students who showed me around the university. Thank you very much for an interesting day.' Smile, shake hands (if appropriate – if you are being interviewed by a panel of five, who are all sitting at the other end of a long table, then don't!) and say goodbye.**

The selectors will have a set of questions that they may ask, designed to assess your suitability and commitment. If you answer *'Yes'* or *'No'* to most questions, or reply only in monosyllables, they will fire more and more questions at you. If, however, your answers are interesting and also contain statements that interest them, they are more likely to pick up on these, and you are, effectively, directing the interview. If you are asked questions that you have prepared for there will be less time for the interviewers to ask you questions that might be more difficult to answer.

For example, at the end of your answer to a question about work experience, you might say: *'...and the physiotherapist was able to explain the effect of new technology on physiotherapy.'* The interviewer may then say: *'I see. Can you tell me about how technology is changing physiotherapy?'* You can then embark on an answer about ultrasound, for instance. At the end of your explanation you could finish with: *'...of course, ultrasound treatment is often used in conjunction with infrared radiation treatment.'* You may then be asked about situations where this might happen, and so on.

Of course this does not always work, but you would be very unlucky not to have at least one of these 'signposts' that you placed in front of them followed.

HOW YOU ARE SELECTED

During the interview the panel will be assessing you in various categories. Whether or not the interview appears to be structured the interviewers will be following careful guidelines so that they can compare candidates from different interview sessions. Some panels adopt a conversational style, whereas others are more formal. The scoring system will vary from place to place but, in general, you will be assessed in the following categories:

- reason for your choice of university
- academic ability
- motivation for physiotherapy
- awareness of physiotherapy issues
- personal qualities
- communication skills.

You are likely to be scored in each category, and the university will have a minimum mark that you will have to gain if you are to be made an offer. If you are below this score, but close to it, you may be put on an official or unofficial waiting list. If this happens you may be considered in August, should there be places available.

If you are offered a place you will receive a letter from the university telling you what you need to achieve in your A-levels. This is called a Conditional Offer. Post-A-level students who have achieved the necessary grades will be given Unconditional Offers. If you are unlucky all you will get is a small brown envelope from UCAS saying that you have been rejected. If this happens it is not necessarily the end of the road that leads you to a career in physiotherapy. You may be successful in Clearing, or as a post-A-level applicant. The way to go about this is described on page 36.

When UCAS has received replies from all of your choices they will send you a Statement of Offers. You will then have about a month to make up your mind about where you want to go. If you only have one offer you have little choice but to accept it. If you have more than one you have to accept one as your Firm choice, and another (usually a lower offer) as your Insurance choice. If the place where you really want to study makes a lower offer than one of your other choices do not be tempted to choose the lower offer as your Insurance, since you are obliged to go to the university that you have put as your Firm choice if you achieve the grades. Even if you narrowly miss you may still be accepted by your first choice. If you decide that you do not want to go there, once the results are issued, you will have to withdraw from the UCAS system for that year.

CASE STUDY

Tania

Tania's first encounter with physiotherapy came as a result of a knee injury and this encouraged her to investigate the profession more thoroughly. She was lucky in that her school had a very active Science Society, and she was able to attend lectures by a physiotherapist and a reflexologist. Tania chose her A-level subjects – biology, chemistry and sports studies – with physiotherapy in mind, and was able to arrange a variety of work experience placements including a spell at St Thomas' Hospital in London, a hydrotherapy placement, shadowing an occupational physiotherapist at Shell, and sessions with a physiotherapist who specialised in maternity problems and with a sports physiotherapist.

Tania applied to four universities and chose Birmingham, because 'it has a good reputation within the profession, and because it was highly recommended by students who had studied there.' Birmingham also offered work placements in the first year of the course, which is 'quite a scary prospect now, but seemed a good idea before applying!'

Tania is enjoying the course: 'It is interesting as there are lots of practicals, lots of anatomy and a lot of self-learning – all of which makes it hard work as well.' Studying physiotherapy does have its downsides, however. Compared with students doing other courses, the physiotherapy students work long hours, and have to take in a large amount of factual material. 'Quite overwhelming at times,' says Tania.

Tania was interviewed both as part of a group, where she had to talk about a personal experience of physiotherapy, and on her own. In her individual interview she was asked whether she had ever failed anything and what she then did about it; and why she chose physiotherapy rather than medicine or dentistry.

Tania's long-term plans include a two-year NHS spell and then, hopefully, working abroad for a while – possibly in South Africa, New Zealand or Canada. Tania's advice for prospective physiotherapists is: 'do as much work experience as possible so that you can relate what you learn to what you can see.' She also advises students to look at some anatomy before they start the course so that it does not come as too much of a shock.

RESULTS DAY

The A-level results will arrive at your school on the third Thursday in August. The universities will have received them a few days earlier. You must make sure that you are at home on the day the results are published. Don't wait for the school to post the results slip to you. Get your teachers to tell you the news as soon as possible. If you need to act to secure a place you may have to do so quickly.

The university admissions departments are well organised and efficient, but they are staffed by human beings. If there were extenuating circumstances that could have affected your exam performance and which were brought to their notice in June, it is a good idea to ask them to review the relevant letters shortly before the exam results are published.

If you previously received a Conditional Offer and your grades equal or exceed that offer, congratulations! You can relax and wait for your chosen university to send you joining instructions. One word of warning: you cannot assume that grades of AAC satisfy an ABB offer. This is especially true if the C grade is in biology.

The following paragraphs take you through the steps necessary to use the Clearing system because you have good grades but no offer. They also explain what to do if your grades are disappointing.

WHAT TO DO IF YOU HAVE GOOD GRADES BUT NO OFFER

These days very few applicants get into university through Clearing. Very few universities have spare places in August and, of those that do, most will choose to allow applicants who hold a Conditional Offer to slip a grade rather than dust off a reserve list of those they interviewed but didn't make an offer to. Still less are they likely to consider applicants who appear out of the blue – however high their grades. That said, it is likely that every summer one or two universities will have enough unfilled places to consider a Clearing-style application.

If you hold, say, AAB but were rejected when you applied through UCAS you need to let the universities know that you are out there. The best way to do this is by fax. Fax and phone numbers are listed in the UCAS *Handbook*. If you live nearby you can always deliver a letter in person, talk to the office staff and hope that your application will stand out from the rest.

Set out on page 37 is a sample letter/fax. Don't copy it word for word!

Don't forget that your UCAS referee may be able to help you. Try to persuade him or her to ring the admissions officers on your behalf – he or she will find it easier to get through than you will. If your headteacher is unable/unwilling to ring, then he or she should, at least, fax a note in support of your application. It is best if both faxes arrive at the university at the same time.

If you are applying to a university that did not receive your UCAS form ask your head to fax or send a copy of the form. In general it is best to persuade the university to invite you to arrange for the UCAS form to be sent.

If, despite your most strenuous efforts, you are unsuccessful, you need to consider applying again (see below). The other alternative is to use the Clearing system to obtain a place on a degree course related to physiotherapy and hope to be accepted on the physiotherapy course after you graduate. This option is described on page 44.

Your name
Address
Telephone number
Date

Miss M D Whyte
Admissions Officer
Melchester University School of Physiotherapy
Address

Dear Miss Whyte

UCAS No. 1234567

I have just received my A-level results, which were:
Biology B, Chemistry B, English C
I also have an A grade in AS Photography

You may remember that I applied to Melchester but was rejected after
interview/was rejected without an interview. I am still very keen to
study physiotherapy at Melchester and hope that you will consider
me for any places that may now be available.

My headteacher supports my application and is faxing you a
reference. Should you wish to contact him, the details are:
Mr C Harrow, Tel: 0123 456 7891, Fax: 0123 456 7892.
I can be contacted at the above address and could attend an interview
at short notice.

Yours sincerely
[Your signature]
Your name

WHAT TO DO IF YOU HOLD AN OFFER BUT YOUR GRADES ARE DISAPPOINTING

If you have only narrowly missed the required grades (this includes the
AAC grade case described above) it is important that you and your

referee fax the university to put your case before you are rejected. Another sample letter follows below.

Your name
Address
Telephone number
Date

Miss M D Whyte
Admissions Officer
Melchester University School of Physiotherapy
Address

Dear Miss Whyte

UCAS No. 1234567

I have just received my A-level results, which were:

Chemistry B, Biology B, English C

I hold a conditional offer from Melchester of ABB and I realise that my grades fall below that offer. Nevertheless I am still determined to study physiotherapy and I hope you will be able to find a place for me this year.

May I remind you that at the time of the exams I was recovering from glandular fever. A medical certificate was sent to you in June by my headteacher.

My headteacher supports my application and is faxing you a reference. Should you wish to contact him, the details are:
Mr C Harrow, Tel: 0123 456 7891, Fax: 0123 456 7892.
I can be contacted at the above address and could attend an interview at short notice.

Yours sincerely
[Your signature]
Your name

If this is unsuccessful you need to consider retaking your A-levels and applying again (see below). The other alternative is to use the Clearing system to obtain a place on a degree course related to physiotherapy and hope to apply to the physiotherapy course after you graduate. This option is described on page 44.

RETAKING YOUR A-LEVEL(S)

The grade requirements for retake candidates are often higher than for first timers. You should contact the universities to find out what they require from retake students. Many A-levels can be retaken in January, but this depends on the board as well as the subject. The school or college where you will sit the retakes will be able to help you. The timescale for your retake will depend on:

- the grades you obtained first time
- the examination board you studied.

If you simply need to improve one subject by one or two grades and can retake the exam on the same syllabus in January then the short retake course is the logical option. If, on the other hand, your grades were DDE and you took your exams through a board that has no mid-year retakes you probably need to spend another year on your retakes. You would find it almost impossible to master syllabus changes in three subjects and achieve an increase of nine or ten grades within the 17 weeks or so that are available for teaching between September and January.

Independent sixth-form colleges provide specialist advice and teaching for students considering A-level retakes. Interviews to discuss this are free and carry no obligation to enrol on a course, so it is worth taking the time to talk to their staff before you embark on A-level retakes.

CASE STUDY

Trevor

Trevor is in his first year at Bristol UWE. However his route in reaching this stage was not a standard one.

After gaining nine GCSEs at grade C or above Trevor moved into the sixth form at his school already aware that he wanted to study physiotherapy and so he chose to study biology (a course requirement) as well as mathematics and computing. Preparation, both academically and through work experience, was going well but unfortunately a very serious illness in the family during the later parts of his upper sixth year had a detrimental effect on his final A-level results (Trevor had been predicted B grades but achieved D grades).

At this stage Trevor had to decide what to do, and after thinking about it and discussing it with his family he chose to retake his A-levels and apply for physiotherapy the following year.

Trevor joined a sixth-form college and began one-year courses in biology, mathematics and psychology. He chose psychology instead of computing because he did not enjoy the latter and because he thought psychology would be both more relevant and more useful when he became a physiotherapist.

He thought very carefully about his choice of universities, investigating them in depth through prospectuses, the Internet and by visiting as many as he could. Trevor was an active sportsman and had to undergo physiotherapy as well as being able to observe it in action. His mother worked as an occupational therapist and so he was able to gain extended experience at four major hospitals in the London area. In his words: 'This was absolutely invaluable in showing me I wanted to study physiotherapy.' This experience was divided between working in mental health and working in the community in order to get a real feeling for 'getting information across' and 'working as part of a team'.

Trevor achieved ABC in biology, mathematics and psychology respectively and having firmly accepted a place at Bristol UWE joined them last September. He is absolutely convinced that 'getting out there and finding out about the subject' was vital to his successful application.

RE-APPLYING TO UNIVERSITY

The choice of universities for your UCAS form is going to be narrower than it was the first time round. Don't apply to the universities that discourage retakers unless there really are special, extenuating circumstances to explain your disappointing grades. The following are examples of excuses that would not be regarded by admissions tutors as extenuating circumstances:

> 'I went to Barbados at Easter and my files got soaked when a freak wave took me by surprise when I was revising on the beach.'

> 'I left my bag on the bus the week before the exams, and all of my notes were in it, so I couldn't do any revision.'

'We moved house a month before the exams and a removal man trod on my notes, so I couldn't revise properly from them.'

Some reasons are acceptable to even the most fanatical opponents of retake candidates:

- your own illness
- the death or serious illness of a very close relative.

These are just guidelines, and the only safe method of finding out if a university will accept you is to write and ask them. A typical letter is set out on the opposite page. Don't follow it word for word and do take the time to write to several universities before you make your final choice.

Notice that the format of your letter should be:

- opening paragraph
- your exam results – set out clearly and with no omissions
- any extenuating circumstances – a brief statement
- your retake plan – including the timescale
- a request for help and advice
- closing paragraph.

Make sure that your letter is brief, clear and well presented. You can type or word-process it, if you wish, but you should write 'Dear Sir/Madam' and 'Yours faithfully' by hand. If you have had any previous contact with the admissions staff you will be able to write 'Dear Miss Whyte' and 'Yours sincerely'. Even if you go to this trouble the pressure on universities in the autumn is such that you may receive no more than a photocopied standard reply to the effect that, if you apply, your application will be considered.

Apart from the care needed in making the choice of university, the rest of the application procedure is as described in the first part of this book.

Your name
Address
Telephone number
Date

Miss M D Whyte
Admissions Officer
Melchester University School of Physiotherapy
Address

Dear Miss Whyte

Last year's UCAS No. 1234567

I am writing to ask your advice because I am about to complete my UCAS form and would very much like to apply to Melchester.

You may remember that I applied to you last year and received an offer of BBB/was rejected after interview/was rejected without an interview.

I have just received my A-level results, which were:
Biology C, Chemistry C, English E
I was aged 17 years and six months at the time of taking these exams.

I plan to retake Biology in January after a 17-week course and English over a year. If necessary, I will retake Chemistry in the period from January to June. I am confident that I can push these subjects up to ABB grades overall.

What worries me is that I have heard that some universities do not consider retake candidates even when the exams were taken under the age of 18 and relatively high grades were obtained. I am very keen not to waste a slot on my UCAS form (or your time) by applying to schools that will reject me purely because I am retaking.

I am very keen to come to Melchester, and would be extremely grateful for any advice that you can give me.

Yours sincerely
[Your signature]
Your name

NON-STANDARD APPLICATIONS

So far, this book has been concerned with the 'standard' applicant: the UK resident who is studying at least two science subjects at A-level and who is applying from school or who is retaking immediately after disappointing A-levels. The main non-standard categories are as follows.

Those who have not studied science A-levels

If you decide that you would like to study physiotherapy after having already started on a combination of A-levels that does not fit the subject requirements for entry to university, you have three choices. You can either spend an extra year studying science A-levels at a sixth-form college that offers one-year AS/A2 courses (independent sixth-form colleges offer one-year A-level courses and certain subjects can be covered from scratch in a single year – only very able students can cover A-level chemistry and biology in a single year with good results. You should discuss your particular circumstances with the staff of a number of colleges in order to select the course that will prepare you to achieve the A-level subjects you need at the grades you require); you can follow a Foundation course at a university that will then allow you to study a related degree course afterwards, or you can enrol on an Access course which is recognised by the universities you wish to apply to. For details of Foundation courses you should contact universities. Each university will have different policies about Access courses – you should contact the physiotherapy departments directly.

Overseas students

The competition for the few places available to overseas students is fierce and you would be wise to discuss your application informally with the university before submitting your form. In general, overseas applicants will find it difficult to gain a place unless they can offer qualifications that are recognised by the universities, such as A-levels or the IB.

Information about qualifications can be obtained from British Council offices, or British Embassies, and from the universities that offer physiotherapy courses.

Overseas students are liable for the full cost of tuition. For physiotherapy the fees vary, depending on the university, but will be in the region of £10,000 per year.

Mature students and graduates

Each year a small percentage of the entrants to physiotherapy are aged 22–30. In exceptional circumstances candidates who are over 30 may be considered. In general there are two types of mature applicants: graduates, and mature students with no suitable academic qualifications.

Graduates
An upper second class degree or higher is normally required. Most universities ask graduates to take a year out between the final year of their first degree course and the start of the physiotherapy course in order to get work experience. This allows them to demonstrate that they are serious about a career in physiotherapy. Applicants without a degree with a significant biological content may be asked to take an A-level in biology and to achieve a B grade or higher.

Applicants with no suitable academic qualifications
Candidates are likely to be asked to sit at least two A-levels, one of which will be biology, and to achieve B grades or higher. There are also some Access courses that can lead to an offer of a place to study physiotherapy; applicants should liaise with universities to confirm suitability.

The main difficulty facing those who come late to the idea of studying physiotherapy is that they rarely have a scientific background. They face the daunting task of studying science A-levels and need very careful counselling before they embark on what will, inevitably, be quite a tough programme. Independent sixth-form colleges provide this counselling as part of their normal interview procedure.

CASE STUDY

Alice

Alice is in her first year at St George's Hospital Medical School. Alice is a talented sportswoman, and whilst she was at school she competed regularly at national level. Because of the commitment to training that this required she spent longer studying

44

for her A-levels than a typical student. She applied for a place to read physiotherapy as a mature student. As well as a wealth of first-hand experience of physiotherapy (having recovered from injuries and having been shown the correct way to avoid injuries during her competition years) she also had a week of work experience at a large busy hospital in Middlesex. In discussion it was easy to see that she had a good idea of the breadth of opportunities within the field she wanted to study at university.

Alice chose St George's Hospital Medical School because she felt it offered 'early and very good clinical contact, training alongside other healthcare professionals and because they were the most helpful prior to submitting my application'. She is very happy with her course although she didn't particularly enjoy the common core studied at the start of the first year with all the other students in the medical field. Although it was a good general introduction she is much happier now that she is concentrating on the study of physiotherapy and its applications. She says that she is really glad she spent a long time studying the prospectuses, looking at websites, talking to physiotherapy students, coaches, admissions tutors and her college because it helped her make a very informed decision and allowed her to pick the course she thought most suited her.

Alice was interviewed for a place and felt that her knowledge of the course, range of work experience and a strong UCAS form and references helped her to feel confident and to come across as someone who was well prepared and who was capable of tackling the physiotherapy course at St George's. Alice thought that support for her application was very important but that ultimately the decision to study physiotherapy was an informed one and had to be her own.

STUDENTS NOT STUDYING A-LEVELS

As with A-levels, entrance requirements will vary from university to university. The information below is given as a guideline only.

- **BTEC National/Higher National Diploma or Certificate**: a distinction/merit profile throughout the course.
- **Advanced GNVQ**: merit/distinction in science plus A2 level in an academic subject. Optional units should have a biological emphasis. Students who have studied the GNVQ in Health and Social Care are usually required to have an A2 in biology or a related subject.
- **Irish Leaving Certificate**: six papers taken at one sitting at Higher Level to include AABB or 400+ points, and to include a biological science.
- **Scottish Highers**: AABBB to include a biological science.
- **IB**: 32 points with a grade 6 in biology.
- **European Baccalaureate**: 75 per cent to include a high mark in biology.

USEFUL INFORMATION

TYPICAL COURSE STRUCTURE

Whilst all physiotherapy courses contain many common elements there are significant differences in the structure of these courses, in the course content, in the way in which the practical and patient contact elements are arranged, and in the styles of assessment. You should investigate this thoroughly by reading prospectuses and looking at the physiotherapy departments' websites in order to find out which ones will best suit you.

First year

Study of the theory and practical issues underlying physiotherapy

- Anatomy
- Physiology
- Kinesiology (the study of the mechanics of body movement)
- Research methods
- Musculoskeletal conditions
- Cardiovascular and respiratory functions
- Communication and clinical skills.

Second year

The second year course divides the time between academic study and clinical placements. Clinical placements take place in a variety of settings, including hospital wards, physiotherapy outpatients departments and specialised units within hospitals and the community. The clinical placements will focus on areas such as orthopaedics, rehabilitation and community medicine. Chartered Society of Physiotherapy guidelines require a certain number of hours (1000) of clinical practice to be undertaken in order to gain recognition, and the 16 weeks of clinical placement are usually in the order of 30 hours per week.

- Neurology
- Clinical education, taking into account social, cultural and economic factors
- Pathophysiology
- Clinical placements.

Third year

The third year will also be split between clinical and academic study. Specialist areas could include outpatients, neurology, respiratory medicine, mental health, learning difficulties and paediatrics. Students will usually spend about 20 weeks of the course on clinical placements.

- Pain management
- Exercise science
- Neurorehabilitation
- Option topics such as sports science, burns and plastic surgery, mental health
- Clinical placements.

Elective clinical placement

At the end of the third year there might be an elective clinical placement. The students choose the speciality in which they wish to work and arrange the placement themselves. Many choose to work abroad, or in areas of health care not previously encountered in their own clinical education.

CURRENT ISSUES

Technology in physiotherapy

Enter the words 'physiotherapy' and 'news' into an Internet search engine and most of the links that you get are to news stories about new forms of treatment. Although the basic techniques used in physiotherapy have been around for a long time – physical manipulation, repetition of exercises and other forms of manual therapy – technology plays an increasing part.

Probably the most widely used application of technology within physiotherapy is ultrasound. Ultrasound treatment utilises high-frequency (up to 3MHz – too high for the human ear to hear) sound waves. Ultrasound is used extensively in medicine for diagnosis either to form images in order to see what is happening inside the body (for instance, scans that show the foetus inside the womb of a pregnant woman) or to measure blood flow. Whenever ultrasound waves pass from one tissue to another a small percentage of the beam is reflected back, and these reflected sound waves are used to create a picture, or to measure the speed that blood is flowing (using something called the Doppler Effect).

Ultrasound can also be used therapeutically, that is, for treatment. Ultrasound has been used to accelerate tissue repair and to relieve pain since the 1950s. It is used to treat a variety of conditions such as sports injuries, sprains, tendonitis, arthritis, ulcers, and to relieve the pain associated with, for instance, phantom limbs in amputees. The sound waves penetrate deep into the body and, although the biological effects are not completely understood, it is likely that the vibration caused by the sound waves produces a combination of heating (thermal effects) and stimulation of tissue and blood vessels (mechanical effects). Ultrasound is usually given at the end of a course of treatment, following other forms of manual therapy.

Ultrasound equipment is relatively cheap to buy (less than £2000 for an ultrasound machine) and is easy to use. The total cost to the NHS of ultrasound in physiotherapy is around £5 million per year – a tiny proportion of the total NHS bill. The drawbacks of the extensive use of ultrasound in physiotherapy are that there is little conclusive clinical evidence that it is effective; and that there is a possible risk of tissue damage if the power settings on individual machines are not accurately calibrated. An evaluation report on the therapeutic use of ultrasound can be found on www.epi.bris.ac.uk/

Increasingly, robots are being used in physiotherapy. This does not mean that next time you require physiotherapy you will be treated by R2D2, Bender or Kryton. The effective rehabilitation of patients following a stroke, cerebral palsy or brain injuries requires repetitive movement exercises and controllable resistance to motion. In one such treatment the patient is coupled to a robot joystick that guides him or her through a series of movements. The robot can be programmed to vary the scope of the movement, to increase or decrease the resistance, or to help the patient to complete the movements. To increase interest levels for the patient the movements can be integrated into a 'game' on a screen in front of the patient. In this way tens of thousands of therapeutic movements can be completed over the course of a few weeks – far more than the physiotherapist could manage, and more than the patient is likely to be able to accomplish alone.

Another new development is in the use of high-energy shockwaves to relieve complaints such as tennis elbow (epicondylitis), reducing the need for physiotherapy, osteopathy or surgery. Based on the technology used to destroy kidney stones, the machine (sold under the name ReflecTron) sends shockwaves into the body that vibrate tissue. The makers claim that this increases blood flow and helps to encourage the production of cells and the regeneration of tissue. The exact mechanisms are not fully understood, but research carried out at London's Imperial College suggest that the treatment is effective.

RSI

Repetitive Strain Injury, or RSI, is an increasingly common complaint amongst computer users. As the name suggests, the condition is caused by repetition of certain movements, usually associated with computer keyboard use. However, it is not confined to computer users, and has been diagnosed in many people whose jobs involve manual labour or machine operation. The condition can also occur when the person's posture is inappropriate to the task that he or she is undertaking. RSI manifests itself as pain, mostly when the task that caused it is being carried out, but often at other times as well. It usually affects the neck, shoulders, elbows, wrists or hands. RSI is also known by other names including Repetitive Stress Injury, WMSD (work-related musculoskeletal disorder), WRULD (work-related upper limb disorder), CTD (cumulative trauma disorder) and OOS (occupational overuse syndrome). The term RSI actually encompasses a number of different conditions, most commonly Carpal Tunnel Syndrome. Carpus comes from the Greek word 'karpos', which means wrist. The joint in the wrist is surrounded by fibrous tissue, and there is a small gap between this tissue and the bone, through which a nerve (the median nerve) passes. The nerve then splits to serve the fingers and thumb. Repetitive movement of the wrist can cause swelling of the tissue in the wrist, putting pressure on the median nerve. Symptoms include numbness and tingling in the fingers and thumb, followed by pain. The condition can usually be cured by a combination of physiotherapy and rest.

Not everyone believes that RSI actually exists. Carpal Tunnel Syndrome certainly does and can be caused by obesity, arthritis, diabetes and pregnancy, but there are those who are sceptical as to whether repetitive movement is a cause. A report in the *British Medical Journal* on research done at Manchester University cast some doubts about RSI. The research indicated that the majority of those who suffered from arm or wrist pain (105 people in a survey encompassing 1200 volunteers) were also the most dissatisfied with their jobs and who suffered from high stress levels. In other words the pain could be due to psychological or stress factors rather than simply the physical aspects of their jobs.

Rehabilitation of stroke patients

A stroke occurs when a blood clot blocks a blood vessel in the brain, causing brain cells in the area to die. If treatment is not given immediately, further cells in the surrounding areas also die. The functions, such as speech, memory or movement that were controlled by these brain cells are then affected, depending on the area of the brain where the blood vessels were blocked. The severity of the stroke can vary from patient to patient, and the effects may be very minor (and temporary) or they may lead to paralysis or death.

The main types of rehabilitation are:

- Physical therapy – to improve mechanical skills such as walking, use of the hands, or balance.
- Occupational therapy – to re-learn the skills that are required for everyday life such as eating, dressing and looking after oneself.
- Speech therapy – often, the power of speech is lost and patients need to re-learn how to communicate effectively.

Physiotherapy for stroke patients must begin as early as possible following the stroke in order to be effective. Improvement is slow and recovery is difficult six months after the stroke. However, paralysed muscles cannot be treated too early or they may be permanently damaged. Research carried out at the University of Texas, reported in *New Scientist,* found that rats and monkeys which had received small brain injuries to cause paralysis of a limb suffered further injury if treatment was started immediately. The researchers surmised that glutamate, a neurotransmitter that is released during movement, was the probable cause since, in large concentrations, it acts as a toxin. Brain damage appeared to multiply its effects. Research is now being carried out to find drugs that will block the effects of glutamate.

The expertise of the physiotherapist is vital in assessing when (and in what form) treatment should start. At the start of the treatment, the physiotherapist will prepare muscles for the more intensive treatments that will follow, and will work on enabling the patient to support his or her own weight if leg muscles are affected. The later stages of physiotherapy may involve compensation for permanently damaged muscles through the introduction of aids such as walking frames. The physiotherapist may work alongside occupational therapists, speech therapists, carers and psychologists to try to prepare the patient for a return to 'normal' life.

COURSES AND GRADE REQUIREMENTS

You are advised to check the UCAS *Handbook* or website for information on courses and universities before applying.

Institutions offering physiotherapy courses

University of Birmingham
Tel: 0121 414 3344
Website: www.bham.ac.uk

University of Bradford
Tel: 01274 233081
Website: www.brad.ac.uk

University of Brighton
Tel: 01273 600900
Website: www.brighton.ac.uk

Bristol UWE
Tel: 0117 3443333
Website: www.uwe.ac.uk

Brunel University
Tel: 01895 203214
Website: www.brunel.ac.uk

Coventry University
Tel: 024 7663 1313
Website: www.coventry.ac.uk

University of East Anglia
Tel: 01603 456161
Website: www.uea.ac.uk

University of East London
Tel: 020 8223 2835
Website: www.uel.ac.uk

Glasgow Caledonian University
Tel: 0141 331 3000
Website: www.gcal.ac.uk

University of Hertfordshire
Tel: 01707 284800
Website: www.herts.ac.uk

University of Huddersfield
Tel: 01484 422288
Website: www.hud.ac.uk

Keele University
Tel: 01782 584005
Website: www.keele.ac.uk

King's College London
Tel: 020 7836 5454
Website: www.kcl.ac.uk

Leeds Metropolitan University
Tel: 0113 283 3113
Website: www.lmu.ac.uk

University of Liverpool
Tel: 0151 794 2000
Website: www.liv.ac.uk

University of Manchester
Tel: 0161 275 2077
Website: www.man.co.uk

University of Northumbria at Newcastle
Tel: 0191 2274472
Website: www.unn.ac.uk

University of Nottingham
Tel: 0115 951 6565
Website: www.nottingham.ac.uk

Oxford Brookes University
Tel: 01865 483040
Website: www.brookes.ac.uk

Queen Margaret University College, Edinburgh
Tel: 0131 317 3247
Website: www.qmuc.ac.uk

Robert Gordon University
Tel: 01224 262105
Website: www.rgu.ac.uk

University of Salford
Tel: 0161 295 5000
Website: www.salford.ac.uk

Sheffield Hallam University
Tel: 0114 2255555
Website: www.shu.ac.uk

University of Southampton
Tel: 023 8059 5000
Website: www.soton.ac.uk

St George's Hospital Medical School
Tel: 020 8725 5201
Website: www.sghms.ac.uk

University of Teesside
Tel: 01642 218121
Website: www.tees.ac.uk

University of Ulster
Tel: 02870 324221
Website: www.ulst.ac.uk

University of Wales College of Medicine
Tel: 029 2074 2027
Website:www.uwcm.ac.uk

Grade and subject requirements for physiotherapy courses 2002

The grade requirements listed here are correct at the time of going to press. You are advised to contact the universities before completing your application to check that they have not changed.

University	A-level Grades/Tariff	A2 Biology*?
Birmingham	300–340	Grade B
Bradford	300	Grade B
Brighton	300	Yes
Bristol UWE	300–350	Grade B
Brunel	300–350	Grade B
Coventry	BBB	Not specified
East Anglia	300	Grade B
East London	300–360	1 Science
Glasgow Caledonian	CCC	1 Science
Hertfordshire	320–360	Grade B
Huddersfield	CCD	Yes
Keele	300	Yes
King's College London	ABB	2 from Bio, Maths, Physics, Chem

Leeds Metropolitan	300	1 Science
Liverpool	300	Grade B
Manchester	BBB	Grade B
Northumbria	180–280	Physical or Behavioural Science
Nottingham	BBB	Grade B
Oxford Brookes	BBB	Grade B
Queen Margaret	ABB	2 from Bio, Maths, Physics, Chem
Robert Gordon	ABB	2 Sciences
Salford	300	Grade B
Sheffield Hallam	BBC	Yes
Southampton	350**	1 Science
St George's Medical School	300	Grade B
Teesside	280	Grade B
Ulster	AAA/AAB	1/2 Science
UWCM (Cardiff)	310	Yes

* In some cases universities will accept a biological science, such as human biology, in place of A-level Biology. You should check the university prospectuses for details.

** All AS levels at C or above.

FURTHER READING/USEFUL ADDRESSES

An essential starting point is the **Chartered Society of Physiotherapy**'s website (www.csp.org.uk). The website carries detailed information about careers in physiotherapy and about recognised courses. The CSP also produces many useful booklets about physiotherapy. They can be contacted at: Chartered Society of Physiotherapy, 14 Bedford Row, London WC1R 4ED. Tel: 020 7306 6666; Fax: 020 7306 6611.

The **Irish Society of Chartered Physiotherapists**' website address is: www.iscp.ie/content/.

The **College of Occupational Therapists**, 106–114 Borough High Street, London SE1 1LB. Tel: 020 7357 6480.

The **Society of Chiropodists and Podiatrists**, 53 Wellbeck Street, London W1M 7HE. Tel: 020 7234 8620.

For information on university applications contact **UCAS** (www.ucas.co.uk). The UCAS website has a search facility that will enable you to check the latest entrance requirements for all universities that offer physiotherapy courses. Application materials can be obtained from: UCAS, PO Box 28, Cheltenham, Glos GL50 3SA.

For detailed information on all physiotherapy courses consult *Degree Course Offers* written by Brian Heap and published by Trotman (www.trotmanpublishing.co.uk, Tel: 020 8484 1150).

Other useful addresses

NHS bursaries
NHS Student Grants Unit
Room 212C
Government Buildings
Norcross
Blackpool FY5 3TA
Tel: 01253 332 697

The NHS (Wales) Student Awards Unit
Human Resources Division
The National Assembly for Wales
Cathays Park
Cardiff CF10 3NQ
Tel: 029 2082 6886

Student Awards Agency for Scotland
3 Redheughs Rigg
South Gyle
Edinburgh EH12 9HH
Tel: 0131 476 8212

For visually impaired applicants
Royal National Institute for the Blind
Physiotherapy Support Services Manager
224 Great Portland Street